Best wish

Based on a True Story

THE MEDALLION

By Plato Papajohn

The Medallion
Based on a true story

Copyright © 2012
By: Plato Papajohn

Copyright Claim
TXU00190A399

Cover Design by Plato Papajohn and Derek Gaylard
Photography by Ted Tucker, Birmingham, Alabama

Printed in the United States of America
Printed By Rocky Heights Print and Binding, LLC
Printing Number 10 9 8 7 6 5 4 3 2 1
This book is typeset in Adobe Garamond Pro

DEDICATION

This story is dedicated to the memory of Father Pierre—who he was will forever remain a mystery. The actual medallion featured in the story burns as brightly today in my mind as it did in 1919 when Father Pierre gave it as a gift to the woman who would become my mother-in-law.

PUBLISHER'S NOTE

The Medallion is based on a true story. The names of the characters in the story, with the exception of Father Pierre, are fictitious. Any resemblance to any person, living or dead, is purely coincidental.

SUMMARY

In The Medallion, Plato Papajohn recounts the story of a medallion that was given to him by his mother-in-law just before she died. Urging Plato to always keep the mysterious metal pendant close to him, she entrusted it to his care in the hope that it would bring the same peace and comfort that she firmly believed it had brought her in the years that she had treasured it.

Plato chronicles the journey of the medallion beginning with the bizarre circumstances under which his mother-in-law received it from a priest in a miracle church in France. His story carries the reader through the events that led him to break his vow to his mother-in-law and pass the medallion on to a close friend whose abiding love for his father convinced Plato of the higher calling for which the medallion may have been meant.

CHAPTER ONE

"Plato," she whispered, "I have something I want to give to you."

Our world holds countless mysteries and unexplainable phenomena. Science over the centuries has drawn back the veil on many natural wonders that surround us and has developed the technology that has taken us from the depths of Earth's oceans to the outermost reaches of our universe.

Sometimes, however, we encounter the most minor occurrences in our daily lives that must remain at the outer limits of our ability to comprehend and accept. If humans had answers to all the questions that continuously bewilder us, we would not, by definition, be humans.

I have always believed that everything that happens to and around us is for a reason and part of a "Grand Plan." The events surrounding the medallion at the heart of this story falls into the category of those inexplicable incidents that we choose to either believe or to question.

I believe them.

That belief led me to document this story in its entirety exactly as I experienced it. My belief, however, does not provide an explanation. I leave it to the reader to arrive at a conclusion or explanation for what happened or, like me, to forever wonder.

October 31, 1954 was one of the most important days of my life. On that day, I gave up the single life to marry the woman who had stolen my heart. Xanthie was a stunningly beautiful seventeen-year-old woman who agreed to walk down the aisle and enter a new life with me as Mr. and Mrs. Plato Papajohn. Our wedding vows were exchanged in the traditional ceremony of the Greek Orthodox Church in Birmingham, Alabama where Xanthie and I had met. Though very small with only family and a few close friends in attendance, the wedding was beautiful and filled with symbolism and ceremony that marks the celebration of the sacrament of holy matrimony for orthodox Christians.

Xanthie and her sister had been living with their mother, Christina, in the Five Points South neighborhood of Birmingham. After the excitement of our wedding reception wound down, we drove my freshly washed 1952 Pontiac to Xanthie's home so that she could complete packing for the week-long honey-moon we had planned in Orlando, Florida. It was almost nine thirty at night by the time we had zipped shut the last suitcase. Despite the lateness of the hour, we wanted to leave the same evening to maximize our time in Florida.

My mother-in-law had baked an apple pie earlier that day and had served us a generous slice along with coffee while we had been puttering around the house gathering the last of our things.

"Plato, I've got just a couple of last-minute items to throw into my bag and I'll be ready," Xanthie announced. "Sit with Mama just a minute and I'll be right back."

As soon as Xanthie had left the room, my mother-in-law smiled and turned toward me. "Plato," she whispered, "I have something I want to give to you."

Surprised at her slightly secretive tone, I wondered what she had saved to present to me at just that moment. I thought that it might be some family heirloom or possibly an envelope with some extra money to supplement the modest amount I had been able to salt away for our trip. I was running a small produce business at the time, which provided a decent living, but did not allow for much in the way of luxuries. I was touched that she would want to give us some of her small savings to ensure that we would have a memorable honeymoon.

She walked over to a desk in a corner of her living room. With a solemnity that almost hypnotized me, she opened a drawer in the desk and extracted a small, wooden box. Opening the box, she carefully removed what looked to be a coin the size of an American silver dollar. Holding the shiny gold-colored coin as if it were a treasure, she carefully placed it in my hand.

My mystification as to what the treasure was must have been evident on my face.

Mother," I said, "this is the most beautiful coin I have ever seen. What is it?"

"It is not a coin," she explained. "This is a medallion. I have carried it with me constantly since it was given to me in 1919 when I was a twenty-five-year-old girl. That was thirty-five years ago. Even today, I go nowhere without it. It is always with me. At bedtime, I put it under my pillow when I sleep."

My confusion continued. "What is the difference between a coin and a medallion?" I asked.

She smiled her motherly smile. "A coin is a piece of precious metal of fixed weight and value," she said.

"This medallion is different. It is not a unit of currency. It has a special meaning.

"What is its meaning," I asked, with my curiosity growing by the minute. "And why are you giving it to me at this time, especially since it has so much meaning to you?"

She took my hand in hers. "I am giving it to you now as a special gift," she answered. "I have very little in the way of money to give to you and Xanthie to help you begin your life together. This medallion, however, means much more to me than any amount of money. I give it to you now along with a prayer that it brings both of you the good health and happiness that I have been blessed with for most of my life. I have always believed that those are the two greatest blessings that we can receive in this life."

I could feel my throat tightening and my eyes becoming moist.

"Mother, you have given me Xanthie," I said, choking back the rising lump in my throat. "Along with your blessing, that means more to me than any gift you could give us. I accept this medallion in the spirit in which you are giving it and promise to you that I will cherish it forever as you have done. It will always be with me as it has been with you."

She smiled her most matronly smile and continued. "Thank you, Plato. Please be careful never to lose it and keep it with you always."

I leaned forward and kissed her cheek. "It will be with me forever," I promised. Turning the medallion over in my hand, I continued to be intrigued by its beauty. "What is it?" I asked. "And where did you get it?"

"Plato, that's a story for another day. I know that you two are anxious to get started on your honeymoon. Orlando is a long drive. Perhaps when you return, I'll tell you all about this medallion. Xanthie does not know anything about it."

"Mother, you have raised my curiosity to an unbearable level," I assured her. "Please tell me and Xanthie the story. Orlando can wait."

Xanthie entered the room and noticed how enraptured I was with whatever her mother had been telling me.

"What's this?" she asked. "Secrets? Is my mother telling you childhood stories about me?"

"Better than that," I remarked. I showed her the medallion and relayed the bits and pieces of the story that her mother had shared with me so far.

"Well, you positively must tell us the story, Mother," she insisted. "We'll be thinking about this all week while we're gone if you don't."

"Get yourself a drink, sit down, relax and be attentive," she said. "This is an untold and strange tale."

CHAPTER TWO

When you are in love, nothing else matters.

My mother-in-law started relating her story.

"My husband," she began, "Xanthie's father, was named Constantine. Most people called him Costa. Next month will be three years since he passed away.

"Costa came from a small village tucked away in the mountains in the southern Peloponnesus region of Greece. When I say a small village, I mean tiny. It's been there since the Middle Ages, but today it is just a tiny farming community of about 100 whitewashed houses with terra cotta tile roofs. No hotel, no restaurants, just a cluster of farm families who tend their olive trees and goats. Only about thirty people live there in the winter time as weather is pretty harsh. It's very cold and they get a lot of snow in the mountains. In June, July and August, the population swells to about three hundred as families who have summer homes there return for the cool mountain breezes and to escape the heat and tourist crowds of Athens and the larger cities.

"Costa immigrated to the United States around the turn of the twentieth century and became a naturalized American Citizen. He watched as Europe exploded into World War I in 1914, and when the U.S. entered into fighting in 1917, he enlisted in the American Army.

"Costa's unit was sent to Europe and served part of their tour in Belgium. It was there that he and I met. I was a young girl living there at the time and it was easy for me to fall in love with this handsome Greek-American who was serving in the army, helping to liberate Europe. I met him when he passed through our village and it was love at first sight for both of us."

She paused for a moment and looked slightly lost.

"Mother, please go on. You have captured us with this story."

"I'm sorry," she laughed. "Those events seem like a lifetime ago, and when you reach my age, they tend to blur. I can remember being in love, though, as you and Xanthie are right now.

"I was born and grew up in Belgium, and had learned to speak four languages—German, French, English and Flemish. Love is the universal language, however, and Costa and I were very much in love. We saw each other a good deal while he was stationed in Belgium, but, when the war ended, he was scheduled to return to America with his unit. He promised me that he would send me the necessary papers for me to immigrate to the United States so that we could get married.

"True to his word, Costa sent me the papers and in six months, I was headed to American to become his bride. This was 1919 and even though I was twenty-five years old, my parents were very much against me leaving my native country to travel to the United States and marry a soldier I had met.

"I was determined, however, to marry Costa, and nothing they could say would discourage me or make me change my mind. When you are in love, nothing else matters. Love takes control of your life and it certainly had control of mine.

"I immigrated to this strange new land, married Costa and became a naturalized American citizen in my newly adopted country. Costa had settled in Birmingham, Alabama, which had a fairly large Greek community. Many of the Greeks living there had emigrated from his village of Tsitalia in the Peloponnesos. Costa operated a small restaurant on 20th Street in the heart of downtown Birmingham, and I worked with him there. We were very happy in our new life and were anxious to start a family.

"A couple of years passed, however, and try as we may, we were never blessed with children. We went to several medical specialists and each told us the same thing. The problem was not with Costa, they said, but with me. It was just not possible for me to conceive children. They assured us that adoption would be our only option for starting a family of our own.

"With great sadness, we accepted our prognosis and began entertaining the idea of adopting a child. Before we could get the procedure started, however, I received a letter from my mother in Belgium, telling me that my father had been in an accident and suffered a broken arm and leg. She needed help taking care of him. The letter arrived on December twentieth, and, despite being in the midst of the holidays, I immediately made plans to fly to Belgium. I planned to stay about three weeks.

"After arriving in Belgium and being at home with my parents for just a few days, I was sitting with my mother one morning in the kitchen drinking a cup of coffee.

"'Christina,' my mother said, 'you have been married now for better than two years. Are you and Costa considering starting a family?'

"I told my mother what the doctors had told us about not being able to have children of our own. She seemed very saddened to hear the news.

"'That may be true,' she said, 'but before you give up, however, there is something that I would like for you to do for me. And please do not say no.'

"'What's that?' I asked.

"'This may seem like a strange request,' my mother said, 'but before you give up on having your own child, I want you to take a train ride to the south of France.'

"'France?' I asked, totally dumbfounded. 'I don't know anyone in France! Why would you want me to go to France and what would I be doing there?'

"'I know it seems odd,' my mother answered, 'but please do this for me. I want you to go to the village of Lourdes and stay there for three days. There is a grotto where in 1858 the Virgin Mary appeared to a fourteen-year-old girl named Bernadette Soubirous. Thousands of pilgrims go there every year to pray for a miracle. While you are in Lourdes, go every day to the grotto and to the church and pray before the icon of the Virgin Mary. Pray harder than you have ever prayed in your life and ask the Blessed Mother to intercede on your behalf. Ask her to appeal to the Lord to grant your prayer for a child of your own.'

Naturally, I was dumbfounded at her request. "'Mother,' I said, 'this seems almost like a dream. I'm to go to this church and ask for a miracle?'

"'Yes,' she replied immediately. 'Miracles do happen, and the grotto and church attract thousands each year seeking a miracle. Pray fervently and perhaps your prayer will be answered. Perhaps the Lord will grant you a miracle.'

"Somewhat puzzled over my mother's strange request, I nevertheless purchased a ticket two days later at the train station and traveled to Lourdes. As my mother requested, I visited the grotto and went each day to the church and prayed. I prayed so hard that I could almost feel perspiration forming on my forehead. I sat in the pew and prayed, I prayed standing up. I knelt before the icon of the Virgin Mary and prayed.

"As my three-day visit was coming to a close, I visited the church one last time on a crisp, cold, Friday afternoon in January for a final round of prayers. I offered the last of my supplications, crossed myself and rose from the pew to leave. I turned from the altar and started for the door, but stopped suddenly as if I had walked into a wall."

CHAPTER THREE

Miracles happen every day. Sometimes we notice and sometimes we don't.

At this point in my mother-in-law's story, Xanthie and I were riveted to our chairs. We could not have left even if we wanted to. My mother-in-law sensed our captivation with what she was telling us, and she continued.

"Standing before me was an elderly man with the most pleasant countenance I had ever beheld," she said. "Anyone looking at him would have been awash in feelings of calm and peace. His face was a cherubic red and he had a full beard that was as white as a seagull's wing. His eyes were tiny onyx slits. The man was wearing the brown robe of a monk with a white rope around his waist. Startled at first, his smile and calming manner immediately eased my apprehension.

"'Good afternoon, my child,' he said.

"'Good afternoon,' I answered, not knowing if I should address him as 'Father' or 'Brother' or what.

"'My name is Father Pierre. Might I ask you your name?'

"'Of course, Father. My name is Christina.'

"'That is a beautiful name,' he said. 'Do you mind if I ask you another question?'

"'Not at all, Father,' I replied. 'What would you like to know?'

"'My child, I have noticed that you have been coming here every day for the past few days and you appear to be praying very hard. I have been at this church for many years and have seen many people come here to pray. Very few, however, have struck me with the devotion that you seem to have in your prayers. Many come here with various afflictions seeking help from the Blessed Mother for themselves or for a loved one. You appear to be a healthy and very lovely young woman, so I assume you are praying for a loved one. May I ask the nature of your problem?'

"'Father, I am twenty-five years old and am blessed to be in very good health. My doctors have told me, however, that I am unable to have children. My husband and I live in America and have been hoping to start a family, but it appears that is out of the question according to the medical specialists we have seen. My parents live in Belgium, and while visiting them last week, my mother urged me to come here and pray to the Virgin Mary to intercede on my behalf and ask the Lord to grant us a child. She said that this is a church that many people have visited and prayed for miracles that sometimes happen. Is this true, Father?'

Father Pierre smiled and nodded his head. "'Miracles happen every day,' he said. 'Sometimes we notice and sometimes we don't. Most believe that it was a miracle that the Blessed Mother appeared to the little girl in this place a hundred years ago. It is faith that sustains us. Do not lose your faith. Keep praying as hard as you have done these last three days. God surely hears our prayers, and He answers them. It may be in His own way and in His own time, but He certainly answers us. Never stop believing that."

"'Father, thank you so much for your words,' I

said. 'I believe that I was sent here for a reason and you have helped me find that reason. I will continue to pray and hope that God sees fit to grant me my request for a child. I will remember this visit and I will remember you.'

"The old gentleman then extended his hand to me, not to shake it or for me to kiss it as some parishioners do, but to hand me something. He placed a medallion in the palm of my hand and closed my fingers around it. It is the same medallion I have just given you.

"'Christine, this is a gift from me, but all true gifts come from God,' Father Pierre said. 'Take it with you wherever you travel and remember your visit to our church. God go with you.'

"He then turned and walked away. I stood there in silence for a few moments before opening my palm and gazing in wonder at the medallion. I looked at it then with the same astonishment that you are looking at it now. I never saw Father Pierre again, but I never forgot his words. And I have always had the medallion with me since that day so many years ago."

CHAPTER FOUR

There is a baby on the way.

Xanthie and I were spellbound as we listened to her mother tell us the tale of how she came into possession of the medallion she had just given me. All of this was as new to Xanthie as it was to me, her mother never having told her about it before. Orlando was now the furthest thing from our minds. We had to hear more. At our insistence, my mother-in-law continued.

"I took the train back to Belgium from Lourdes and told my mother what had happened," she related. "She just smiled and told me to do as the priest had instructed—continue my prayers and expect a miracle.

"After another week of helping my mother take care of my father, I was again packing my bags and getting ready for my flight back to the United States. Costa met me at the airport when I arrived in Birmingham and I told him about my time in Belgium, but did not mention my experience at Lourdes.

"About three months later, I was waking up each morning not feeling well. I wasn't really sick, but I felt that I was not one hundred percent either. I decided to go see my doctor. The news he gave me was almost beyond belief.

"After examining me, my doctor smiled and gave me the news that I was pregnant! I couldn't believe what I was hearing!

"'I can't explain it either!' my doctor said. 'You were examined before, we ran all the tests, and you got a second opinion before confirming what I had told you. By all accounts, you are not supposed to be able to have a child. But as I just told you, there is a baby on the way.'

"I raced home to tell Costa, and he was as ecstatic as I was. We laughed and danced around like teenagers; and then we prayed. I wanted to thank God for what I was sure was a miracle sent from Him. I don't know if it was the result of the medallion or Father Pierre's insistence on my continuing to pray or just a misdiagnosis from the doctors. Whatever it was, Costa and I were going to have a baby.

"I have to believe that it was not just a coincidence that Father Pierre singled me out to talk to me that day. And I firmly believe that the medallion he gave me, along with the prayers, helped work the miracle. After being told that I would never have children of my own, I was now getting ready to bring my child into the world.

"I can see Father Pierre's face before me right now as clearly as I saw it that day in the church so many years ago: his snow-white beard, his dancing eyes and his peaceful smile. And I can still hear him telling me not to lose my faith. I am convinced that God answered my prayers and granted me that miracle."

By the time my mother-in-law finished the story, it was almost eleven at night. With our car still packed, Xanthie and I went off to bed in her mother's house with her story still vivid in our minds. The drive to Orlando would wait until tomorrow.

I found myself getting as attached to the medallion as my mother-in-law had become over the years. True to my promise to her, I began carrying it with me in my pocket wherever I went.

And I became increasingly interested in the history of Lourdes and the little girl to whom the Virgin Mary reportedly had appeared. Reading everything I could find relating to the incident, I learned that that grotto and church have become one of the most visited pilgrimage shrines in the Christian world. Between February 11 and July 16, 1858, young Bernadette saw the apparition of a white-robed lady a total of sixteen times in a small grotto along the bank of the Cave de Paul River near the town of Lourdes in the South of France.

In each experience, the Virgin told Bernadette to tell the village priest to build a chapel on that site and people would come there to worship. On the occasion of her fifteenth appearance to Bernadette, the lady revealed herself to be the Virgin Mary.

Bernadette was supposed to have walked a short

distance from where the vision had appeared and suddenly knelt and begun digging in the ground with her hands. A small pool of water soon appeared and over the next few days, the puddle deepened and spread and became the sacred spring for which the town is now famous.

Over the next few years, the site served primarily as a pilgrimage destination for people in the surrounding area, but its fame quickly spread. Soon, people from all over France were traveling there. After numerous healing incidents were reported at the spring, the story of Lourdes and its miraculous powers spread far beyond the south of France. The grotto and the church at Lourdes developed a reputation worldwide for their spiritual and therapeutic powers.

Pilgrims in increasing numbers began flocking to the site in the hope that its unexplained healing powers might result in a miracle for themselves or for a loved one. Construction began in 1876 of an immense church with seating capacity for more than two thousand worshippers. While visitors usually begin arriving in the spring, a continuous stream of the faithful files through the church and the grotto throughout the summer months. Many times their visits coincide with the Feast of the Assumption on August 15, the Feast Day of the Virgin Mary. The piety, devotion and fervent prayers of these visitors have made the shrine of Lourdes one of the most visited Christian sites in the world.

CHAPTER FIVE

There are lots of things I can give you, but the medallion is not one of them

From the time my mother-in-law gave me the medallion until a certain day in 1959, I was never without the medallion. I carried it everywhere I went. On the rare occasion where I might be working around the house or engaged in some activity where I did not have it physically with me, I felt that something was missing.

During that five-year period, I began playing poker every Saturday afternoon with a group of longtime friends. We rotated the site of our games, sometimes at my house and sometimes at the home of my poker buddies. These came to be fun, relaxing afternoons with a group of close friends, not serious, high-stakes poker events. Normally, our games had a $20 limit per hand.

Each time we began our sessions, I would remove the medallion from my pocket and place it near my chips in front of me at the table. I promised myself that whatever I won at our games, I would send to my brother-in-law in Greece. He was the principal of the elementary school in my village where I grew up and he was very appreciative of the school supplies he was able to purchase with my "winnings." I also regularly sent some of the money to my mother. She enjoyed distributing it to the children of the needy families who lived in the small villages scattered throughout the mountains.

Surprisingly, I developed quite a reputation for my ability to win at our games more often than I would lose. As a matter of fact, my winnings during those years, despite the low-stakes nature of our games, came to more than seventy-five thousand dollars. I know that for a fact, because I kept a detailed account of the amount I was sending to my mother and my brother-in-law. What I will never know, however, is whether my good fortune was due to my skill as a poker player or because my medallion was sitting right in front of me at each game. Most of my friends attributed it to the latter.

Also during those years, I expanded the wholesale produce business that I operated when Xanthie and I married in 1954. I was delivering fruit and vegetables to most of the hotels and restaurants in the Birmingham area, and people came to know me as Plato the Greek.

An event took place while I was delivering produce on a Saturday morning in 1959 that would have a far-reaching impact on my life and on the medallion, which by now, I had come to treasure. A friend of mine, Louis Zamman, was making plans to open a restaurant on Twentieth Street and Sixth Avenue South in downtown Birmingham called The Coalyard. Scheduled to open his doors for the first time the following Monday, I was delivering the fruit and vegetables he would need two days prior to his gala opening.

Pushing my hand truck loaded with crates of lettuce, tomatoes, peppers, carrots, and other vegetables through his kitchen, I noticed numerous floral arrangements in the dining area. Examining the cards attached to them, I found the flowers that had been sent by friends, family and other well-wishers extending their congratulations to Louis on his new business venture. Louis happened to pass by me while I was reading the cards.

"You know, Greek, all my friends except for you sent me flowers to celebrate my grand opening," Louis said, addressing me as "Greek" as he always did. "You're the only one who didn't send me anything. You must still have the first dime you ever made since you came over from Greece."

"I'm not in the same tax bracket as your other friends and vendors!" I responded. "I'm still a small potato trying to make a living!"

"Greek, I'll bet you have more money in your pocket right now than I have in mine," Louis said.

"Take a look at this," I said, emptying my pockets

for him to see. Turning them out, I showed him that I had no money at all with me, only the medallion, which had dropped to the floor.

"What's that?" Louis asked.

I showed him my medallion.

"That's the most beautiful coin I've ever seen. Where did you get it?" he asked.

I told him it was a medallion and not a coin and that it had a long and interesting history.

"Since you didn't send me any flowers, why don't you just give me the medallion instead?" he asked.

I smiled and shook my head. "There are a lot of things I can give you," I said. "But this medallion is not one of them."

"Well, now you have my curiosity up," he said. "Have a cup of coffee with me and tell me about it."

I accepted his offer of coffee and told him where

I got the medallion. As I progressed into the history of the medallion, he became increasingly interested. He kept prodding me to tell him more. Soon, we had drained an entire pot of coffee and the rest of my Saturday deliveries were put on hold until later that afternoon.

At the end of my story, Louis shook his head. "Greek, obviously this medallion has some strange, mystical powers, and it appears to have brought you good luck over the years. Why don't you let me keep it for a while and maybe it will be a good luck charm for me and my new business?"

"Louis, I have never been without this medallion since it was given to me. I just can't give it away."

"You won't be giving it to me," he said. "Just let me keep it for awhile. I'd like to see if it really is a good luck piece."

I turned the medallion over in my hand, studying the design that I had wondered over so many moments during the time that I had owned it. It still shone bright gold in color. One side had an image of a winding road leading to a church that had three windows and a giant double door with an image of a cross on it. "Lourdes" was inscribed across the bottom. The other side had an image of the Virgin Mary framed by a halo.

Reluctantly, I handed it to Louis.

"You have to promise me that you'll take good care of it," I said. "Please, please, please, be careful not to lose it."

"Greek, I see how much this medallion means to you," he said. "I promise to take good care of it. And I will let you know it if brings me the same joy and the same good fortune it has brought you."

"That's a deal," I said, smiling and extending my hand.

CHAPTER SIX

The family tells us he appears to be sleeping.

A month after the grand opening of Louis' restaurant, he had yet to return my medallion. Each time I dropped by to deliver vegetables, he asked me to let him keep it just a while longer. He claimed that his new restaurant was doing much better than he or any of his friends had anticiapated. He attributed his good fortune to my medallion.

"Come on, Greek," he begged. "Let me keep it just a little longer. Things are going great here, and I'd hate to break my string of good luck."

I relented, but chided him each time that he better not get too attached to the medallion, as I was determined to have it back. He promised he would return it soon.

One month later, I stopped by Louis' restaurant on a Saturday morning and had a cup of coffee with him. Sensing that I was there for my medallion, he offered me a deal.

"Listen, Greek, I have really become attached to that coin or medallion or good luck piece, or whatever you want to call it," he said. "How about selling it to me?"

"Louis!" I exclaimed, visibly startled, "You're a close friend of mine, and if I couldn't give you the medallion, how can you possibly think I would sell it? Not a chance!"

"You won't believe how attached I've become to

the thing," he insisted. "And I feel certain that it has been responsible for the terrific start we've had here at the restaurant. How about letting me keep it for just seven more days? A week from today, you drop by, and I promise I'll return it to you. What do you say?"

I thought for a moment. "You better let me see the medallion," I said. "I want to make sure you haven't lost it and are just stalling for time until you find it."

He pulled it from his pocket.

"See? It's not lost," he laughed. "Like you, I carry the thing with me everywhere I go. What do you say, one more week?"

"Louis," I smiled, "nobody can say no to you. I'll be back here next Saturday morning. We'll have coffee again, and I'll get my medallion back. I don't feel like I'm properly clothed now that I don't have it with me."

Louis extended his hand. "It's a deal. I'll have a

week to begin cutting my ties to your medallion and will return it to you then. Thanks for sharing your good fortune with me."

"There's nobody I'd rather share it with," I smiled.

Leaving Louis' restaurant, I reflected on our conversation. I wondered if he was really convinced that the medallion was responsible for bringing him good luck in his restaurant business, or if it was just a coincidence. And was he really getting attached to it?

I would never find out.

On the Tuesday following our Saturday coffee together, I stopped by Louis' restaurant to make an unscheduled delivery. Jamie, his manager, had phoned my office and left word that they had run out of a few items, and he needed me to deliver them as soon as possible. I was surprised when I rang the bell at the delivery door and his manager opened it for me.

"Hi, Jamie. Where's my buddy?" I asked. "He's usually here by now. I don't see him around."

Jamie's face was somber.

"Plato, I've got some bad news," he said. "Mr. Zamman had a massive heart attack yesterday afternoon while he was on the golf course. He's in intensive care at University Hospital. No visitors. They're just allowing immediate family in for about a half-hour twice a day. We're all very worried."

I was stunned. The uncertainty of life, I thought. Just two days ago, Louis and I were laughing over a cup of coffee. Today, he's fighting for his life in an intensive care unit.

"Jamie, I am so sorry," I said. "There's no way for me to get in to see him?"

He shook his head. "Sorry. The family told us to tell everyone to please remember Louis in their prayers, but he's not allowed any visitors while he's in intensive care."

"Tell them we'll be praying for him," I said. "And if there's any change, or if we can do anything, please let me know."

"Thanks, I'll keep you posted," Jamie said.

Three days later on Friday afternoon after I had made my last delivery, I was in the downtown area and decided to stop by Louis' restaurant. I had not heard anything from Jamie and thought I'd check up on Louis myself.

"It doesn't look good," Zoe, the cashier at the register, told me. "The family tells us that he appears to be slipping. It may be that he does not have much longer."

"Zoe, that breaks my heart. Please, let us know if there's anything the family needs or if there's something we can do."

"Thanks, Plato," she said. "We're still praying. We'll let you know if there's any change."

Driving home, I realized that as much as I was concerned about my friend, I was even more worried that I may not get back the medallion I had lent him. I was upset with myself over allowing thoughts to creep into my mind, but they were there nevertheless.

The following morning, the day that Louis was supposed to return my medallion to me, I felt the need to phone the restaurant to inquire about Louis' condition.

Zoe answered the telephone.

"Zoe, this is the Greek. I just called to see how Louis was doing."

"Greek," Zoe sobbed, "he slipped away at nine this

morning. We're pretty much in shock. I'm making a 'closed' sign to place on the front door. The family is making the funeral arrangements right now. Visitation will probably be tomorrow night with the funeral on Monday. We'll probably reopen on Wednesday."

I felt like I had been kicked in the stomach and more.

"Zoe, I am so sorry. Please convey my deepest sympathy to the family. I'll see you at the funeral."

"Thanks," she said. "I'll see you there."

Again, as distraught as I was about losing my friend, I was equally sick about what would happen to my medallion. I wondered who had the medallion now, and how uncomfortable it would be for me to ask for its return.

Xanthie and I went to the visitation on Sunday

night and to the funeral the following afternoon. I saw Louis' wife, Maria, and his son, Joseph, and told them how sorry we were about their loss. It only then hit me how much I would miss seeing Louis at the restaurant. We had much in common. He and I were both immigrants, me from my native Greece and Louis' family from Lebanon. I thought about the many laughs we had shared together over the years and the spirited arguments we had over everything from domestic and international politics to local business strategies. He would be missed.

Equally important to me, and equally embarrassing, was how to go about getting back my treasured medallion. I did not feel comfortable asking the grieving widow for something as seemingly insignificant as that during this very difficult time for her and her family. I asked Xanthie how she felt I should go about it. We decided that I should not say anything about it for a while. Let the healing begin and, at a later date, approach her or Joseph about the medallion and if I could have it back.

That later date, however, seemed to keep getting pushed further and further back. I was still anxious to have the medallion returned, but the time was never right to approach the family about it.

About three months after Louis' death, I heard that the family had decided to sell the restaurant. A developer had plans to raise the building and most of the block to clear the site for a new mixed-use tower that would include businesses, offices and residential lofts. My opportunities for approaching his wife and son about my medallion were diminishing.

My devotion to the medallion and my fascination with it, however, were not.

CHAPTER SEVEN

She just closed her eyes and went to sleep.

Three years after Louis died and my medallion drifted off into obscurity, Xanthie's mother began having chest pains and difficulty breathing. We took Christine to the hospital, and the doctors told us she had advanced heart disease. Due to her age and overall physical condition, they did not believe she could survive an operation that might or might not be succesful in improving her heart function.

Xanthie and I were with Christina daily at the hospital. We watched as her condition slowly deteriorated and the doctors recommended that we begin making her final arrangements. Her heart was getting weaker each day and we were resigned to the fact that she would not be with us much longer.

On her fourth day in the hospital, Xanthie and I arrived in the morning to spend the day with her.

"How are you feeling, Mama?" I asked as we entered her room with a bouquet of flowers.

She smiled through half-closed eyes, but did not speak. Xanthie kissed her mom's forehead and whispered to me that she was going to the cafeteria to get us a couple of cups of coffee.

When Xanthie left the room, my mother-in-law motioned for me to come close. She appeared to want to tell me something.

"What is it, Mama?" I asked. "What do you want to say?"

"Plato," she whispered, "I'm thinking about the day so long ago when Father Pierre gave me the medallion."

"Do you remember me telling you that story?"

"Of course I remember, Mama. How could I forget something like that?"

She gave me a soft smile again.

"Do you still have it?" she asked in a weak and fluttering voice.

"Of course, Mama," I lied. She was going in and out, unable to think or talk.

My heart was racing in hope that she would not ask me to show it to her. She closed her eyes as if to go to sleep. Her hand slipped from mine, and she was gone as I watched her taking her last breath of life.

Xanthie then returned with the coffee. "She's

gone," I whispered. "She just closed her eyes and went to sleep. An hour ago she was talking to me, and now she is gone."

Xanthie and I stayed there by her bedside for a long time and held her little fragile and bony hand before calling the nurse and telling her that Mother was gone.

Twenty-nine years passed, and I never forgot about my medallion; but resigned myself to the fact that it was gone and I would probably never see it again. But fate has a strange way of steering us down roads that we otherwise never intended to travel.

Xanthie and I were invited by a realtor friend of ours to an open house she was hosting one Sunday afternoon. The home she was featuring was on an estate-sized lot in the Mountain Brook neighborhood not far from Vestavia Hills where Xanthie and I lived.

We steered onto the long, winding driveway and left our keys with a cheerful parking valet who opened the door to the foyer of the massive, two-story home. A number of guests were milling around various rooms of the house, and several had congregated around a bar that had been set up in a corner of the den. We greeted our hostess who shook my hand and quickly whisked Xanthie away to meet a group of people in another room of the house. As she left, I told her I was going to get us a glass of wine from the bar.

I recognized the bartender as a young man named David whom I had known from several other catered affairs that we had attended.

"Hello, David," I said. "Nice to see you again."

"Hi there, Mr. Papajohn. How are you?"

"Fine, thanks. I hope you're the same."

"Doing great. What can I get you?"

"Two glasses of Chardonnay, please."

Waiting for David to pour our wine, I felt a young man tap me on the shoulder.

"Excuse me," he said. "Did he call you Papajohn?"

"That's correct," I smiled. "Not too many people around with a family name like that."

"I was wondering if you were the same Papajohn who used to sell fresh produce to my father when he owned a restaurant downtown."

I looked at the young man trying to remember where I might have met him. "I am, but I'm sorry, I don't remember if we met before."

"It was a long time ago, Mr. Papajohn, and you probably wouldn't remember me. You were a friend of my father's, though, and I remember you from your visits to his restaurant."

My eyes grew wide with amazement. "You must be

Joseph Zamman," I said, "Louis' son!"

"That's right," he answered.

"I think everyone in Birmingham must know you," I laughed. "You have the pub and package store in the Lakeview district of Southside. Everybody knows Joseph Zamman; and everyone in Birmingham is familiar with your trademark 'Hey Baby' greeting that you use to welcome everybody into your place. You're somewhat of a celebrity."

Joseph smiled. "I'm not so sure about that, Mr. Papajohn, but it's nice to see you again after all these years. After my family sold the restaurant, I didn't have much contact with most of the people my father knew when he was in the business. I opened my own place a few years ago and have been lucky that it has taken off the way it has. I only knew you through what my father had told me about this."

He pulled the medallion from his pocket. I stared at it in complete amazement.

"Joseph, it's been thirty years since I've seen that medallion," I said. "I thought I would never see it again. I had loaned it to your father, and, when he died so suddenly, I felt awkward asking your mother about returning it. I have a very sentimental attachment to it that began…"

"Mr. Papajohn," Joseph interrupted, "Excuse me for stopping you, but my father told me just before he died that this medallion was a gift from a friend of his and mentioned your name. He said he had grown very attached to it. I learned later that you were the person who gave it to him."

I was becoming more absorbed into the young man's story, but it became my turn to interrupt him.

"Joseph, please wait just a moment. Let me deliver

this glass of wine to my wife on the patio. I am really interested in continuing our conversation."

"I'll be right here," he said.

Delivering the glass of wine to Xanthie, I hurriedly returned to Joseph who was standing near the bar examining several portraits on the wall.

"Mr. Papajohn," he said before I cut him off.

"Joseph, please call me Plato," I said.

He smiled, "Plato, I'd like to tell you the story of how my father gave me the medallion."

"When my father had his heart attack and was in the hospital, my mother and I were there every day even though we were only allowed to see him for a few minutes twice daily. He was very weak and in and out of consciousness most of the time, but on the morning he died, he was surprisingly coherent.

"He whispered for me to come close as he had

something he wanted to tell me. He asked me to go to the closet and bring him a coin that was in his pants pocket. I did so and brought back the only thing in his pocket—the medallion. He smiled very peacefully. I asked him what it was and he told me it had a very interesting story behind it that he would tell me when he got well. He pressed it into my hand and told me to hang onto it and he would relate the story to me later.

"'It was a gift to me from Mr. Papajohn.'"

"Later that morning, my father passed away. I never learned the full story about the medallion. My attachment to it is from the sentimental significance that my father felt for it. It was the last thing he gave me before he died. Every time I look at it, I think of him."

I looked at the shiny gold medallion in Joseph's

hand. A flood of memories engulfed me, stories my mother-in-law had related and what the medallion had come to mean to me.

"Joseph, I really appreciate you telling me how you came into possession of the medallion," I said. "And I thank you for your willingness to return it to me now, but I want you to keep it."

His eyes grew wide and a puzzled look crossed his face. "You want me to keep it?" he asked. "But it must have great value to you. I wouldn't feel right…"

"No," I said. "I am the one who would not feel right taking it now. I realize that, even though the medallion has been a part of my life and I treasure it greatly, it now has even greater value to you. It is the connection between you and your father. As much as I'd like to have it back, I don't want to break that connection. Your father and I were very good friends, but a son's love for his father far outweighs any friendship. I want you to keep it."

"Mr. Papajohn, Plato," he corrected himself, "I don't know what to say. I don't know how to thank you. I will promise you that I will keep it with me as my father told me to do. And I will remember you for allowing me to keep the medallion as a remembrance of my father."

We shook hands. "I am happy that the medallion has a good home," I smiled. "I'm going to catch up with my wife now. Take care."

I turned and walked to the patio to meet Xanthie.

"Who were you talking to?" she asked.

"A very special young man with an interesting old story," I said.

CHAPTER EIGHT

It just wouldn't have the same meaning to my son or to anyone else.

Eight years passed during which time I never saw Joseph again. I continued to hear about Joseph and his landmark pub on the city's Southside of town, but Xanthie and I were not regulars on the bar circuit around town. I again resigned myself to the fact that the medallion had passed from my possession, but felt good that, at least, it was in the hands of someone who appeared to value it as much as I did.

On a sweltering June day in 1994, I returned

from work one afternoon and noticed that the "For Sale" sign that had been in front of the house next to the one where Xanthie and I lived had a "Sold" attachment across it. It had been vacant for almost a year and, due to the price that the owner was asking, I expected it to remain unoccupied for a long while. I did not see anyone around, however, and wondered who our new neighbors would be.

The following weekend, I went out our front door to retrieve the morning newspaper and several men were unloading furniture from a moving van. I decided to go over and introduce myself to my new neighbors. To my surprise, Joseph Zamman came out of the house and onto the driveway carrying a box.

"Joseph, what a surprise! Looks like we're going to be neighbors!" I said.

He put down the box he was carrying and removed

his gloves. A broad grin flashed across his face.

"Mr. Papajohn—oops, sorry, Plato—I didn't know you lived here. Yes, it does appear that I'm the new kid on your block." We shook hands and he motioned me to a chair in the shade on his patio. "They're still unloading everything, but I think these chairs are clean enough for us to sit."

We sat down and chatted about the neighborhood, the work needed to be done to the house and how excited he was about moving in. He was still a bachelor, he said, having never married and would probably remain single. When we finished chatting, I rose to leave. "I'll go back home now and let you finish your unpacking," I said.

"Wait just a moment," Joseph said. "There's something I want you to see." He reached into his pocket and pulled out the medallion. It shone as brightly as it had the first time my mother-in-law had taken it out of the drawer where she kept it and gave it to me.

"Joseph," I said, "I see you truly are a man of your word. You said that you carried it with you and here you are with it in your hand even as you move into your new house. Aren't you afraid, though, that you might lose it?"

"Not a chance," he smiled. "It goes where I go."

"It certainly does not look any older than when I first saw it."

"It sparkles as brightly today as it did on the day my father gave it to me," he said.

"I feel good that it has a happy home," I said. I look forward to seeing you again when you've moved in. Welcome to the neighborhood."

"Thanks, Plato. It's nice to be here. I'm sure our relationship will be great in the future," Joseph said.

Returning to my home, I told Xanthie who our new neighbor was. The following week, we both went next door to pay a visit to our new neighbor. Xanthie brought him a cake she had baked, and we made him promise to call us if he needed anything as he was getting settled in.

During the next few years, I saw Joseph periodically, but, due to the differences in our ages and the busy schedules both of us kept, I rarely spent a lot of time with him. Mostly, we saw each other while doing yard work or chatting across our decks in our backyards.

On a particularly cold afternoon in January, as I was returning from my mailbox, Joseph stepped out onto his front porch and called to me.

"Plato, do you have a moment?" he asked.

"Sure," I said, walking across my lawn to his house.

"What's happening?"

"Come in," he said. "It's freezing outside." He held the door open for me while I entered his living room.

"Plato, I have always wanted to know something. My father told me when he was dying that the medallion he gave me had a very interesting story. Do you have time to tell it to me?"

I placed my stack of mail on a chair. "I do," I said. "And I'm the only one left who knows."

"Sounds good."

"One beer or two would help me to remember the medallion's story," I said.

Joseph vanished into the kitchen and returned with two Heinekens. He opened one and poured it into an icy mug he evidently kept in his freezer. He opened the other beer for himself and sat back. Then he pulled the medallion from his pocket and placed it on the coffee table in front of us. "I've been wanting to hear this story for a long time."

For the better part of the next hour, and two more beers, I related the story of the medallion to Joseph. I covered it all, from the time my mother-in-law received it from Father Pierre to how she felt it was responsible for her ability to conceive a child; how it brought me the good fortune that I was able to share with the people living in my village in Greece; and finally, how Joseph's father had begged me to let him borrow it in hopes that the good luck would rub off on him.

Joseph looked at the medallion and shook his head.

"Plato, that's an amazing story," he remarked.

"Yes, it is," I agreed.

"There's one thing, though, that bothers me now that I know the story," Joseph continued. "My father knew that you had loaned the medallion to him, yet he did not tell me that. He said it was a gift and that he would tell me the rest of the story later. But 'later' never came. Maybe he intended to tell me it was only on loan after he got out of the hospital. I feel that he should have told me that it was your medallion and that I was supposed to return it to you in case he couldn't. In any event, he never finished the story, and I never really knew that it was not his to give to me. And you were considerate enough not to ask for it during the time my family was grieving. I feel I should return it to you now. I don't feel right in keeping it."

I shook my head. "No," I said. "This medallion has traveled many miles in the almost 100 years that we've known its story. How far it traveled before that, we'll never know. And where it will travel after we're gone is not for us to know either. We all pass through this world on a temporary basis, just a tiny blip on the world's clock. Something like this medallion, however, outlasts us all. We may never know how or when it came to be, who the previous owners were, and the circumstances of how it may have impacted their lives. All we know is that both of us, you and I, treasure the memories it has brought us."

"There was a reason that Father Pierre gave it to my mother-in-law; and there was a reason she gave it to me. My friendship with your father was the reason that I passed it on to him, and his love for you is the reason that you have it now. It obviously has come to mean as much to you as it has meant to everyone who has owned it. I could not take it back now. It is yours to keep and to pass on to whomever you want to give it to. I can only hope that it will mean as much to them as it does to us."

Joseph smiled and looked at the medallion. We both rose from our chairs and shook hands.

"Thank you, Plato," he said. "Thank you for sharing your story and your medallion with me. I know you'll think I'm being selfish. I almost wish I could take the medallion with me to my grave."

The startled look on my face must have been clearly evident to Joseph.

"But that would break the chain!" I said. "If you don't pass it on to someone else, then…"

"I feel so strongly about it," he interrupted, "that even though it is extremely selfish of me, I can't imagine ever giving it to someone else. I'm not sure anyone else will ever be as attached to this medallion as I have become. I don't know if I could ever give it up, even to my own children, if I had any.

"There is such a bond that it has cemented between

me and my father—the last thing he gave me before he died. It just wouldn't have the same meaning to my son or to anyone else. I'd like to have it with me always, and when I die, it will be in my coffin," he said.

"Joseph, if you have decided that you are taking the medallion with you when you go, you better make your plans known to someone in your family. They need to know something like that when they are making the funeral arrangements," I said.

"I'm telling you, Plato," he said with the most serious look I had ever seen on his face. "As long as you know this is what I want, Plato, I know you'll make sure to do it," he said.

"Joseph, you have to tell one of your kin folk. I have no relation to you. I'm just a friend," I said.

"Plato, I do not have to say it to my kin folk. You'll do it. I want nobody else to do it but you, he said.

"Joseph, I think you are losing your mind," I said.

"That is that, Plato," he said.

"Well, Joseph, let me put this in plain English so you can understand a little better," I said. "I'm almost thirty years older than you are. Chances are better than good that I'll be leaving this world before you do."

Joseph smiled. "You may be right, Plato," he said, "but I feel better knowing that you know what I want most."

"Joseph, how about let's meditate over who goes first or who goes last and talk about this subject again sometime," I said.

"That is okay with me," he smiled. "Why not, Plato," he said.

CHAPTER NINE

What appeared to be a coin slipped from his palm.

Two weeks after Joseph and I had our conversation and I told him the story of the medallion, Xanthie and I were returning home after a trip to the grocery store. It was only about eight-thirty in the morning, as we wanted to beat the crowd that would pack the store later in the day.

As we were driving home, we were passed by a fire truck with its siren blaring. Pulling to the side of the road, we were also passed by a police car and what appeared to be an EMT vehicle or ambulance.

In a few minutes, we were turning onto our street and noticed that the emergency vehicles were parked on our block. As we got closer, we could see that they were right in front of Joseph's house next door to us.

I drove into our driveway and parked without putting the car into the garage. Xanthie and I ran next door to see what had happened. The policeman standing at the front door asked me to stand aside as the firemen were bringing a stretcher, oxygen and other items into Joseph's home.

"What happened?" I asked.

"Looks like the man had a heart attack," the officer said.

"Joseph?" I asked incredulously. "I just can't believe it."

"Please keep the area clear, so the technicians can do their work," the officer said.

Xanthie and I walked back to our house in stunned silence. We watched from our driveway as family members arrived and ran into Joseph's house. Finally, after what seemed like hours but was actually only about thirty minutes, the firemen opened the door and wheeled the stretcher to the ambulance. On it was a body covered by a sheet.

The firemen were followed by several people who were obviously family members. They got into a car and followed the ambulance as it sped away. Several people remained in front of the house in a group. They spoke softly, voices lowered as if they were whispering in church.

I walked over and said, "I'm Plato, Joseph's next-door neighbor, and this is my wife, Xanthie. Can you tell us what happened?"

"We're not sure," a tall gentleman with snow-white

hair replied. "We're related to the family. Joseph's brother phoned us right after summoning the paramedics. Looks like Joseph just had a heart attack."

"That just seems impossible," Xanthie said. "We just saw him yesterday. You were talking with him. He was always smiling and laughing. Everybody loved him. Now he's gone. I guess it just shows you how fragile and uncertain life really is."

I said nothing. My silence must have been puzzling to Xanthie.

"Plato, are you okay?" she asked.

"I was just thinking the same thing. Life really is impossible to understand sometimes. We're here today and gone tomorrow," I said.

Suddenly, I stopped dead still.

"What is it?" Xanthie asked. "Something is bothering you. Is it the suddenness of Joseph's passing?"

"The medallion!" I cried. "Now what will happen to the medallion?"

"Plato!" she chided. "That's a terrible thing to be thinking right now! The man just died! And you're wondering how you're going to get your medallion back? Shame on you," she said.

"I can't help it," I said. "Joseph and I talked about it before, wondering what would become of it. Now that he's gone, I can't imagine where it will end up. I've got to…"

"You've got to quit talking like this—that's what you've got to do!" Xanthie snapped. "Forget about the medallion, at least until this man is buried! That's horrible for you to be concerned about your medallion while this man has just died."

We opened the side door to our house and went inside. I did not mention anything else about the medallion to Xanthie, but my mind was racing, trying to figure out a way to get my medallion back.

The following day, I looked in the obituaries section of the newspaper and found the write-up on Joseph. It listed surviving family members and the arrangements for the visitation and the funeral. Visitation was scheduled for five p.m. on Monday with burial the following day.

I looked over the list of surviving family members and decided to check the telephone directory to see if any of them were in the book. The paper listed a brother who lived in Birmingham, and his number was disclosed. I decided to phone.

"Hello," a man's voice said on the other end.
"Hello, is this Mr. Nicholas Zamman?" I said.
"Yes it is. Who is this?"
"My name is Plato Papajohn," I said. "I lived next

door to your brother, Joseph. I am so sorry to hear about your loss. He will be missed by a lot of people."

"Thank you, Mr. Papajohn. I appreciate you phoning."

"Mr. Zamman, I was also a friend of your father's," I continued. "I sold vegetables and fruit to him when he had his restaurant downtown."

"I was very young at the time," he said. "Joseph was my older brother and probably remembered more than I do."

"Yes, I understand. Mr. Zamman, I have another reason for phoning you. You probably do not know anything of a medallion I gave your father years ago so you wouldn't be aware of how your father gave it to Joseph. My reason…"

"You're wrong, Mr. Papajohn," he interrupted. "I have seen the medallion you're referring to several times. Joseph showed it to me, but never told me the story behind it; only that he treasured it because it was the last thing our father gave him before he died. I didn't know you were the one who gave it to our father."

I was elated that Joseph's brother at least knew of the medallion. I almost held my breath as I prepared to ask the next question.

"I'm surprised to hear that you've seen it," I said. "Mr. Zamman," I hesitated, "do you happen to know where the medallion is now?" Again, I held my breath.

"As a matter of fact, I do."

My heart raced.

"I was the one who found Joseph," he said. "My brother hadn't shown up at the bar when his bartender arrived that morning. He tried Joseph's cell phone and his home phone. No answer. Then he called me. I drove over to Joseph's house, and his car was in the driveway. I knocked on the door, but no one answered. I phoned the police, and, when they arrived, I explained my concern over what may have happened to my brother. They allowed me to break a window and we entered the house. Joseph was slumped in his recliner in front of the television."

"The police immediately called the paramedics. The EMT guys later told us that it appeared that Joseph had a massive heart attack while he was watching television the previous night. No pain, no suffering. They gave us a few minutes to say our good-byes to him before they pulled a sheet over the body and wheeled him out on the gurney. We were all crying and hugging each other. As I kissed my brother's forehead and patted his hand, what appeared to be a coin slipped from his palm. Picking it up and looking at it, I realized that it was the medallion he had shown me on several occasions. He had told me that he always had it with him. It was with him then, even as he died."

"Mr. Zamman, I'd like to tell you how it came

into your father's possession and then made its way to Joseph."

"I'd appreciate that," he said. "I've always wondered about it."

I began relating the story to Nicholas, moving quickly over the events pertaining to my mother-in-law, how she gave it to me and the good fortune that it brought me. I explained how his father asked me to loan it to him, the attachment he developed to it and how he passed it on to Joseph. Not sure about whether or not to include the part about Joseph wanting to be buried with the medallion, I decided to go ahead and tell him. When I finished, I waited anxiously for his reaction.

"Mr. Papajohn, I have the medallion," he said. "Joseph never mentioned anything about being buried with it, though. Since you are the one who loaned it to my father, I feel that it's right that you should have it back."

"Nicholas, I will be at the funeral service tomorrow. I would very much like to see the medallion. That's all I ask."

"I'll be happy to show it to you," he said. "I'll see you at the funeral. Thanks again for calling."

CHAPTER TEN

He will rest knowing that it has been returned to its rightful owner.

Xanthie and I arrived at the funeral home on Tuesday afternoon. The huge number of cars in the parking lot attested to the many lives that Joseph had touched over the course of his life. Xanthie and I signed the family's book of visitors and went into the chapel. Joseph's brothers, sisters and extended family members were standing next to the casket, shaking hands with the long line of people who had come to pay their respects. Xanthie and I joined a couple of our friends who were seated in a pew toward the rear of the room to wait for a time to go forward and meet the family.

After chatting with our friends for almost a half-hour, I noticed that the line of visitors had finally shortened. I told Xanthie that I wanted just a moment to speak privately with Joseph's brother, Nicholas.

"But I'd like to pay my respects, too," she said.

"Wait here just for a minute," I said. "I'll be right back, and we'll go up there together."

Xanthie appeared puzzled at why I wanted to talk with Joseph's brother alone, but she agreed to wait for me to come back.

I walked up the aisle and waited my turn to shake hands with the family members. I was anxious, however, to speak with Nicholas. Finally, I walked close to the casket. Nicholas got up from where he was sitting and walked close to where I was standing.

He held out his hand. "You must be Plato," he smiled.

I was shocked. "How did you know?" I asked.

"I'm not sure," he replied. "I just had a feeling it was you. We've only had one conversation on the phone, but I feel as if I've known you for a long time."

We hugged and kissed each other.

"Nicholas, may I call you Nicholas?" I asked.

"Of course," he smiled. "And I'll call you Plato."

"That's great," I said. "Nicholas, I can't tell you how sorry I am about your loss. Actually, Joseph's passing is a loss for the city of Birmingham. He was loved by a lot of people here."

"Thank you, Plato, and yes, he was. My brother never met a stranger. I have something here that I know you are anxious to see."

He reached into the pocket of his jacket and produced the medallion. I looked at it in disbelief. I had been so certain that I would never see it again. It shone as brightly as ever."

"Plato, I want you to have your medallion. You were kind enough to loan it to my father, and he passed it along to Joseph without having the chance to return it to you. I don't know if it had any miraculous powers. None of us will know; but it brought a lot of joy to you and your family and to my father. It seems to have brought even more to Joseph. He will rest well, knowing that it has been returned to its rightful owner. Here it is."

Nicholas held it out for me to take.

I looked at it for what seemed like a long time. The single object that meant more to me than any other material possession in the world was now being returned to me after so many years. I wondered about the long road it had traveled to get back to me and how the uncertainty of life had finally brought it back home. I was engulfed by a sense of relief, knowing that I had never asked Joseph or any of Louis' family to return it to me. It was here now, having traveled from Louis to Joseph and now to Nicholas. I was glad that it had brought them a sense of peace or security or even a bit of luck.

Suddenly, I was shaking my head. I couldn't accept it.

"Nicholas, I can't tell you how much I appreciate your offer to return the medallion to me," I said, "but I can't take it."

He looked puzzled.

"You can't take it?" he said in amazement. "But why? That medallion or coin or whatever it is has meant so much to you. It is yours, and you should have it. I am happy to be able to return it to you."

"And I'll never forget your gesture," I said. "But the medallion has meant so much to so many people who were very close to me, including my mother-in-law, myself, Louis and Joseph. The last time I saw your brother, he told me he wanted to go to his grave with this medallion. I feel the need to grant his request. He didn't know at the time that it would be his final request, but it was. It was his most important link to his father. I feel I would be breaking that connection by taking it now. I would like you to put this medallion in your brother's hand. He will have it with him on his journey that each of us will take someday. I want him to have it when he meets your father in the hereafter. I feel sure they will both be glad it is still in the family."

Nicholas stood for a moment, not quite sure what to do.

"Plato, I'm at a loss for words. I'd be honored to have you place the medallion in my brother's hand.

My father and my brother were both very fortunate to have had you as a friend. And I will now consider you as family," he said.

Nicholas kissed the medallion and handed it to me.

"Nicholas, I want to show this medallion to someone before I place it in your brother's palm. Please do not move from where you stand. I'll be right back."

I walked back to where my wife and my two friends were sitting and showed it to them. I asked them to take a good look on both sides of the medallion and then I walked back to Nicholas. Nobody had any idea of what was going on except for me and Nicholas. I walked close to the casket and bent down to kiss Joseph's forehead. Then I placed the medallion inside his cold and stiff palm. I pressed his hand over the medallion. I walked away and returned to where my wife and two friends were sitting. My mission was finally complete. It was an indescribable feeling of peace and joy for me. I had performed an important task.

Death is nothing at all. It was as if Joseph had slipped away. Whatever we were or meant to be to each other, that we still are. Life meant all that it ever meant. It was the same as it ever was. Joseph and the medallion were forever gone down to the ages of ages and will forever both be out of my sight but will never be out of my mind.

Whenever I pass down the street and look at Joseph's house, I know he is not there, and he'll never be; but I close my eyes, and I can see him standing by his water fountain and greeting me with his husky voice saying, "Hey Baby," and calling me by my familiar nickname of Plato the Greek.

The last people that saw the medallion before I

placed it in Joseph's hand were my wife and our two friends. I do not know why I had to show them the medallion. It was not for any reason, nor did it serve any purpose, but I did it.

After the funeral service was over, my wife and our two friends asked me, "What was going on? What was that all about? Everybody was watching you there by the casket. What did you do?

"It is a long, long uncommon story," I said. "One day I will tell you, or perhaps I will write a book and call it 'The Medallion', and you can read this story."

I asked them to tell me if they could remember what was on the medallion. They told me they couldn't.

"Can you tell me anything about it?" I asked.

"It was a very beautiful and shiny coin—the most beautiful coin we've ever seen," they said.

"At this point, the only thing I can tell you and the only thing I want you to know and remember is that what you saw was not a coin. It was a medallion."

The End

ALSO BY PLATO PAPAJOHN
STAIRWAY TO HEAVEN

This amazing adventure starts just before World War II, on the Greek island of Evia. An eleven-year-old boy named Plato suddenly has the beauty of his beloved island and majestic mountains fall into the hands of the Nazis. This idyllic world turns into a nightmare, and life becomes a struggle to survive. An innocent child is transformed into a cold, unfeeling creature, willing to do whatever is necessary to keep him and his family alive through the horrifying years ahead. For those people who have never felt the cold breath of war, or death and starvation, they cannot relate to the haunted dreams of those who have.

This book shows you many experiences of brutality, intrigue, betrayal, cunning, and revenge. Plato, a survivor, is greatly hardened by the Nazi occupation and the civil war that follows. Now he must travel to a new life here in America, facing many new challenges as he becomes familiar with his new homeland. This is where he questions the purpose of his existence and rediscovers his relationship with God, who he thought had long abandoned him. This journey is a powerful rendering that takes you through the worldly and spiritual life of an extraordinary human being, as he becomes a husband, a father, and a successful businessman. In his new life, Plato finds the true gift that fills him with happiness, joy and love. This story will undoubtedly capture your heart. For more information, go to www.papajohnbooks.com.

ALSO BY PLATO PAPAJOHN
VICIOUS MIND

The Heir apparent to one of the most successful cotton empires in the South, Bill grew up with
a father too busy expanding the family business and
a mother who could not control him. Given neither
discipline nor direction, Bill followed his own self-
indulgent impulses, recklessly careening through life
in the fast lane, the pursuit of pleasure his only talent.
By the time he lands in his thirties, Bill has earned a
reputation as a free-wheeling high roller who always

gets what he wants—until he meets the cool, confident and captivating Judy Freeman.

Intelligent and independent, Judy refuses Bill's advances, which only serves to fuel his desire. He sets about redefining his playboy image, wooing her with newly minted integrity and old-fashioned romance, demonstrating his respect and fidelity by promising to bring her into the Wilson Industries...and the Wilson family.

But, just as he has done throughout his life, Bill relies on deception to forge his relationship with Judy. As Judy is drawn into his web of lies, Bill entwines her in his real quest: the acquisition of wealth he believes to be his birthright and power that would put him above the law. Driven by these twin obsessions, Bill finds himself traveling down a road to self-destruction that threatens to destroy the family name and the financial legacy built upon the backs of three generations of Wilsons. For more information, please visit www.papajohnbooks.com.

ALSO BY PLATO PAPAJOHN
THE AVENGER

Melissa Sanders had it all. With a devoted and successful husband, a darling daughter who brought her joy every day, and a gorgeous home in an exclusive neighborhood, life was good…until a brutal act of violence stole her husband's life…and changed her life forever.

This was not the first time violence had touched Melissa's life. Her father, a third-generation police officer, was gunned down in the line of duty, his assailant never apprehended. Powerless as a child to avenge her father's murder, Melissa, a former cop herself, vowed to do whatever it took to find her husband's killer and deliver her own style of justice.

The Avenger takes the reader on a fast-paced ride as Melissa tracks her prey down a twisted trail into the underbelly of criminal life. From the sleazy hangouts of the big city to the decadent pleasures of casinos on the Gulf Coast, Melissa must surrender to the seamy, seedy life of an outlaw to find that man who killed her husband…and make him pay for his crime. For more information, please visit www.papajohnbooks.com.

ALSO BY PLATO PAPAJOHN
THE UNEXPECTED

The Unexpected is a story of trial and tribulation under horrendous circumstances during World War II in Greece, but the novel is also a heart-warming love story. The action begins when sixteen-year-old Christos Christopoulos must decide if he wants to aid a dying Italian soldier in Evia. Arriving on horseback at the site of the soldier's ambush, Christos is mistaken for an angel.

In the Italian soldier's pocket is a photograph of

his beautiful fifteen-year-old daughter, Marcella. Through an amazing series of events, Christos grows up to become a sea captain who one day lands in the port of Genova, the hometown of Marcella. From that point on, the reader is immersed into the blending of two cultures, Greek and Italian. Soon the moment of truth comes for Marcella. Will she marry the man with whom she has fallen so deeply in love or continue to live without the love of her life? The suspense builds when her father decides to visit Evia to relive the moment when he was saved by an angel. For more information, please visit www.papajohnbooks.com.

ALSO BY PLATO PAPAJOHN

Savannah Incident

Based on a true story

In his Savannah Incident, Plato Papajohn weaves a true story of a man troubled by an event which took place over 45 years ago but continues to haunt him today.

The story revolves around a terrible tragedy, the loss of four children in a drowning accident. His desire to recount the events of the tragedy to his priest brings out many unsolved mysteries surrounding the investigation of the drowning—mysteries that include what he feels are instances in which the children have attempted to contact him from beyond.